THE
BIG BOOK OF
PHONICS

Written by
Betty Pollard

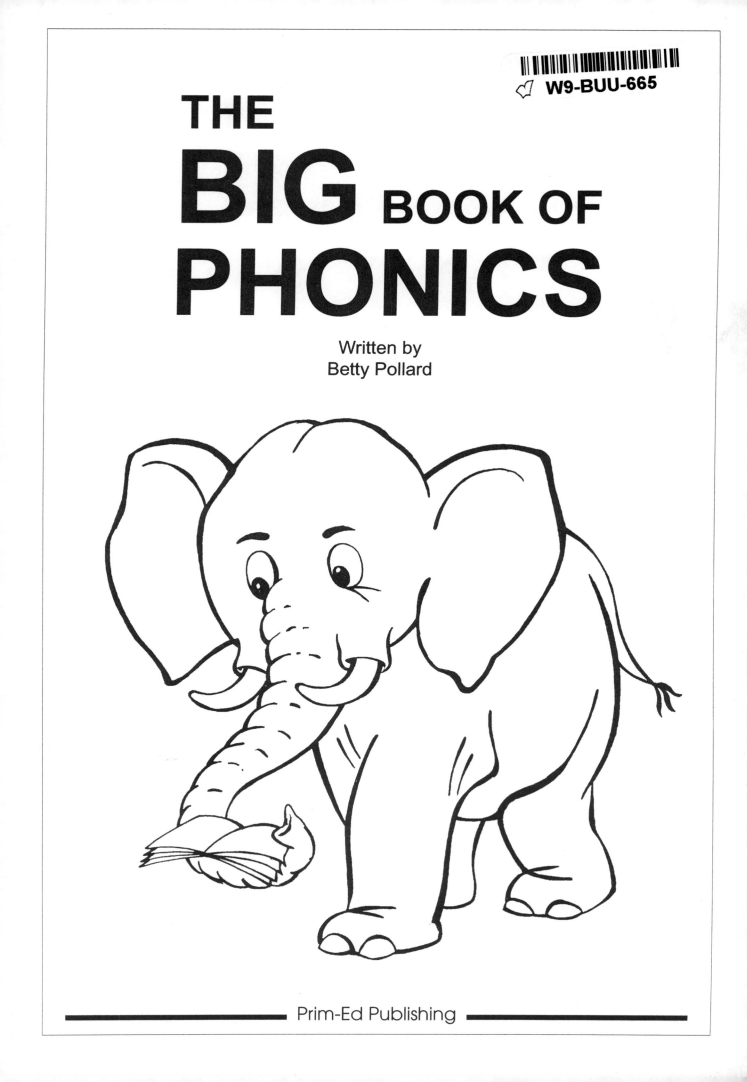

Prim-Ed Publishing

THE BIG
BOOK OF
PHONICS

By Betty Pollard

PR–0134
ISBN 1-86400-082-1

Prim-Ed
Publishing

9 781864 000825

The Big Book of Phonics
Prim-Ed Publishing Pty Ltd

First Published in 1992 by R.I.C. Publications
Reprinted under license in 1994, 1997 and 1998 by Prim-Ed Publishing

Copyright Betty Pollard 1992

ISBN 1 86400 082 1
PR–0134

Additional titles available in this series are:

The Big Book of Early Phonics
Another Big Book of Phonics

Prim-Ed Publishing Pty Ltd
Offices in: United Kingdom: PO Box 051, Nuneaton, Warwickshire, CV11 6ZU
Australia: PO Box 332, Greenwood, Western Australia, 6024
Republic of Ireland: PO Box 8, New Ross, County Wexford, Ireland

THE BIG BOOK OF PHONICS

As the title suggests, this book is a large selection of activities based on the phonetic sounds of the English language. It is intended that the activities be used as an integral part of early teaching programs and that teachers will use the worksheets and the ideas on each page to help to introduce, teach or consolidate the basic sounds, depending on the needs of their class or of individuals within the class.

The activities are consistent throughout the book to allow for ease of use, and aim to consolidate and extend the vocabulary of young children. The activities also allow for a variety of teaching strategies, including whole-class, group and individual activities.

CONTENTS

'y' as in sky

Put 'y' in the space.

sk ___   m ___   tr ___   sl ___   cr ___

fr ___   b ___   st ___   sh ___   wh ___

sp ___   fl ___   dr___

Put the correct word in the space.

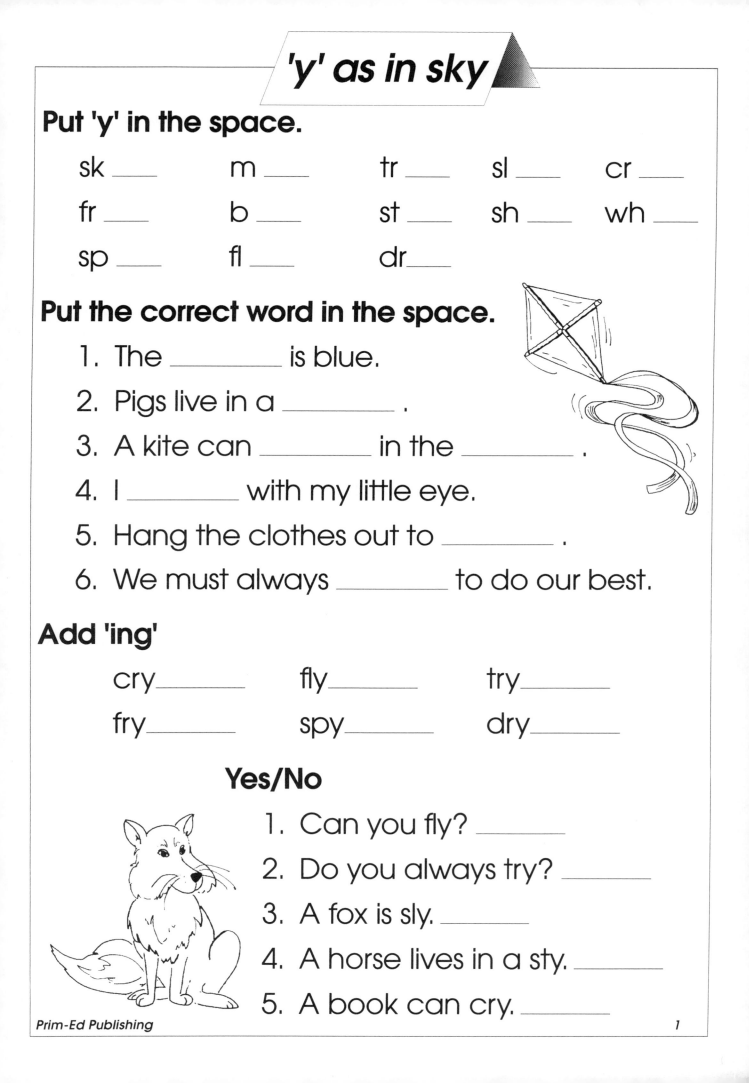

1. The _____ is blue.

2. Pigs live in a _____ .

3. A kite can _____ in the _____ .

4. I _____ with my little eye.

5. Hang the clothes out to _____ .

6. We must always _____ to do our best.

Add 'ing'

cry_____   fly_____   try_____

fry_____   spy_____   dry_____

Yes/No

1. Can you fly? _____

2. Do you always try? _____

3. A fox is sly. _____

4. A horse lives in a sty. _____

5. A book can cry. _____

'y' as in teddy

Put 'y' in the space.

tedd _____   sunn_____   jell _____   kitt_____

pupp _____   spott_____   joll _____   lad_____

happ _____   bump _____   smell _____   gust_____

rust _____   wind _____   rain _____   bab _____

cloud _____   funn _____

Yes/No

1. Have you seen a spotty frog? _____

2. Have you seen a rusty nail? _____

3. Have you been on a bumpy road? _____

4. Have you seen a funny clown? _____

5. Have you eaten purple jelly? _____

6. Have you picked up a puppy? _____

7. Is it windy today? _____

8. Is it sunny today? _____

9. Is it cloudy today? _____

Draw a happy teddy having a picnic on a sunny day.

Put 'll' in the space.

hi ___	be___	do___	bi ___
se___	ro___	fi ___	we___
Po___y	ki ___	fe___	do___y
mi ___	te___	lo___y	ti ___
spe___	wi ___	sme___	gu ___
spi ___	swe ___	du ___	

Put in the correct word.

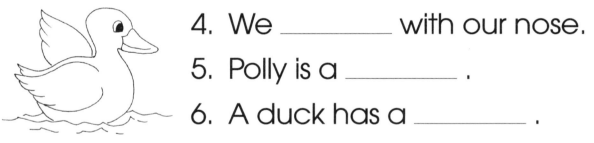

1. Jack and Jill went up the _____ .

2. Do not _____ the milk.

3. We saw a _____ at the beach.

4. We _____ with our nose.

5. Polly is a _____ .

6. A duck has a _____ .

7. At the farm we saw a wind_____ .

8. Our teacher will _____ us a story.

9. I had a ham _____ for lunch.

Draw a windmill on a farm.

'ss' as in hiss

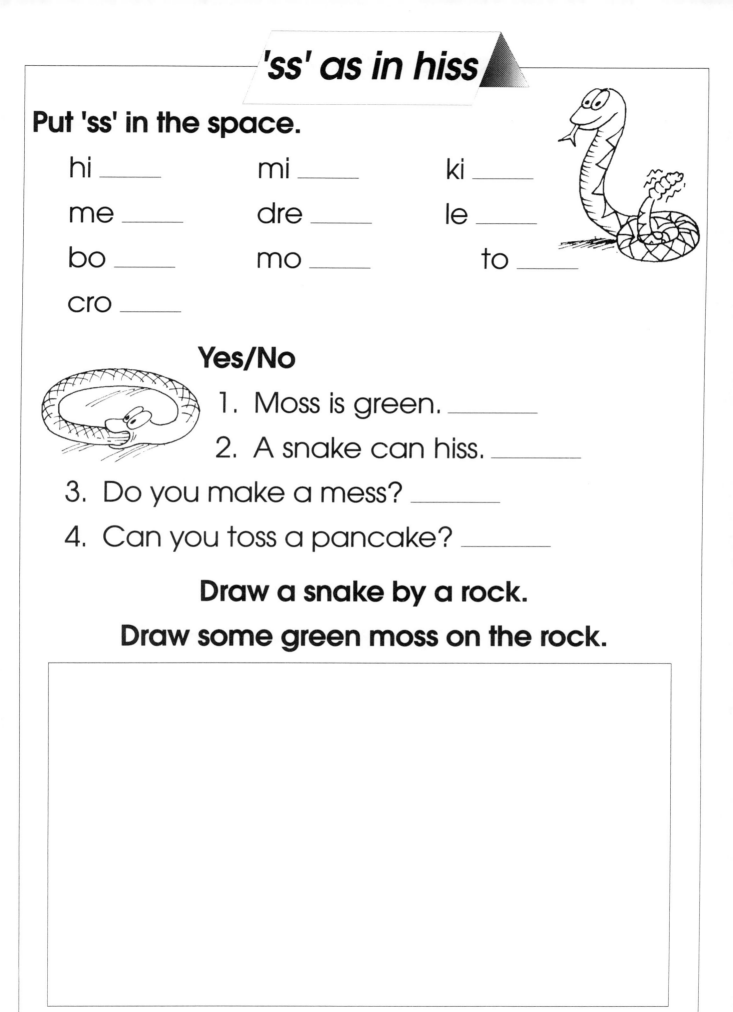

Put 'ss' in the space.

hi _____   mi _____   ki _____

me _____   dre _____   le _____

bo _____   mo _____   to _____

cro _____

Yes/No

1. Moss is green. _____

2. A snake can hiss. _____

3. Do you make a mess? _____

4. Can you toss a pancake? _____

Draw a snake by a rock.

Draw some green moss on the rock.

'e' as in me

Put 'e' in the space.

h ___   m ___   w ___   b ___   sh ___

Put in the correct word.

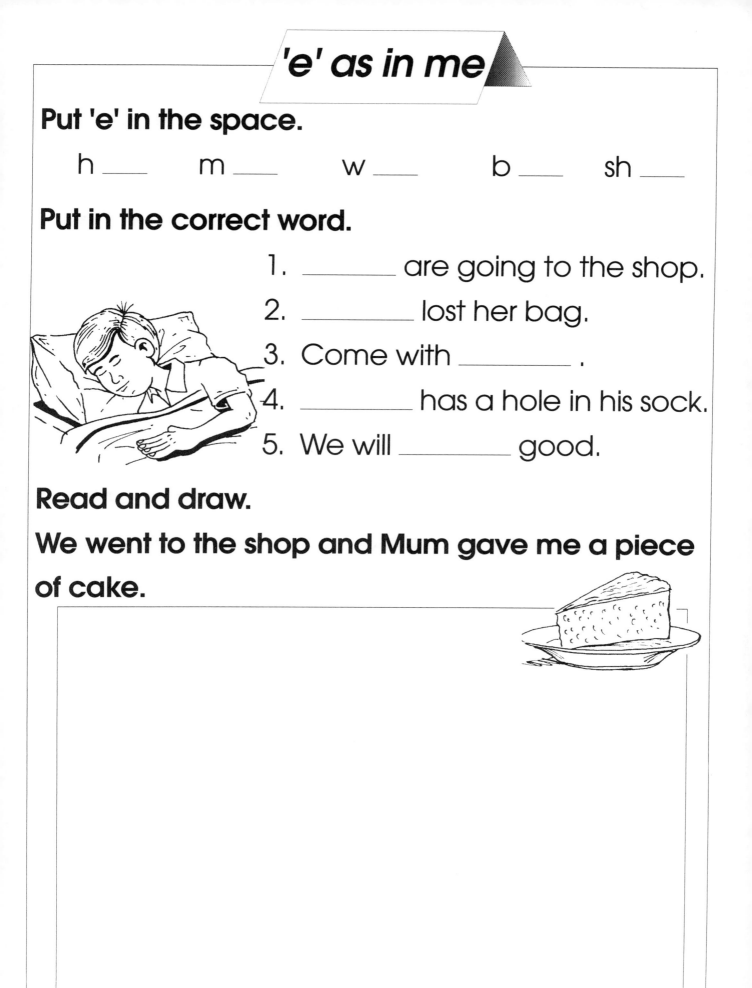

1. _____ are going to the shop.
2. _____ lost her bag.
3. Come with _____ .
4. _____ has a hole in his sock.
5. We will _____ good.

Read and draw.

We went to the shop and Mum gave me a piece of cake.

Put 'ck' in the space.

du _____   Ja _____   si _____   ki _____

sa _____   ba _____   li _____   ro _____

chi _____   lo _____   bri _____   tri _____

clo _____   so _____   ne _____   pe _____

pa _____   ro _____et   po _____et

ti _____–to _____

Put in the missing word.

1. The clock went _____–_____ .

2. Put the _____ with the shoe.

3. _____ and Jill went up the hill.

4. Mother _____ has a duckling.

5. The _____ went up into the sky.

6. We can _____ a ball.

Draw Mother Duck and her ducklings swimming on the pond.

'tr' as in tree

Put 'tr' in the space.

_____ ee _____ ay _____ am _____ ousers

_____ ack _____ ick _____ ip _____ iangle

_____ ickle _____ uck _____ y _____ ap

_____ easure

Put in the missing word.

1. The pirates had some _____ .

2. A clown can do a _____ .

3. A train goes on a railway _____

4. The goat went _____ - _____ over
   the bridge.

Draw a big tree and a little tree.

Make a garden near the trees.

Yes/No

Do you like trees? _____

Are trees important? _____

'pr' as in pram

Put 'pr' in the space.

_____ am	_____ ess	_____ esent
_____ ick	_____ ay	_____ etty
_____ incess	_____ opeller	_____ ickle

Put in the missing word.

1. Peter Rabbit had a _____ in his toe.

2. A _____ lives in a castle.

3. A boat has a _____ .

4. My birthday _____ was a new bike

5. Baby has a _____ .

Draw a castle.

Draw a princess in the castle.

Draw the king and queen.

Put 'fr' in the space.

_____ og   _____ idge   _____ iend   _____ uit

_____ y   _____ ying   _____ ill   _____ ame

_____ ight   _____ ock   _____ eckles

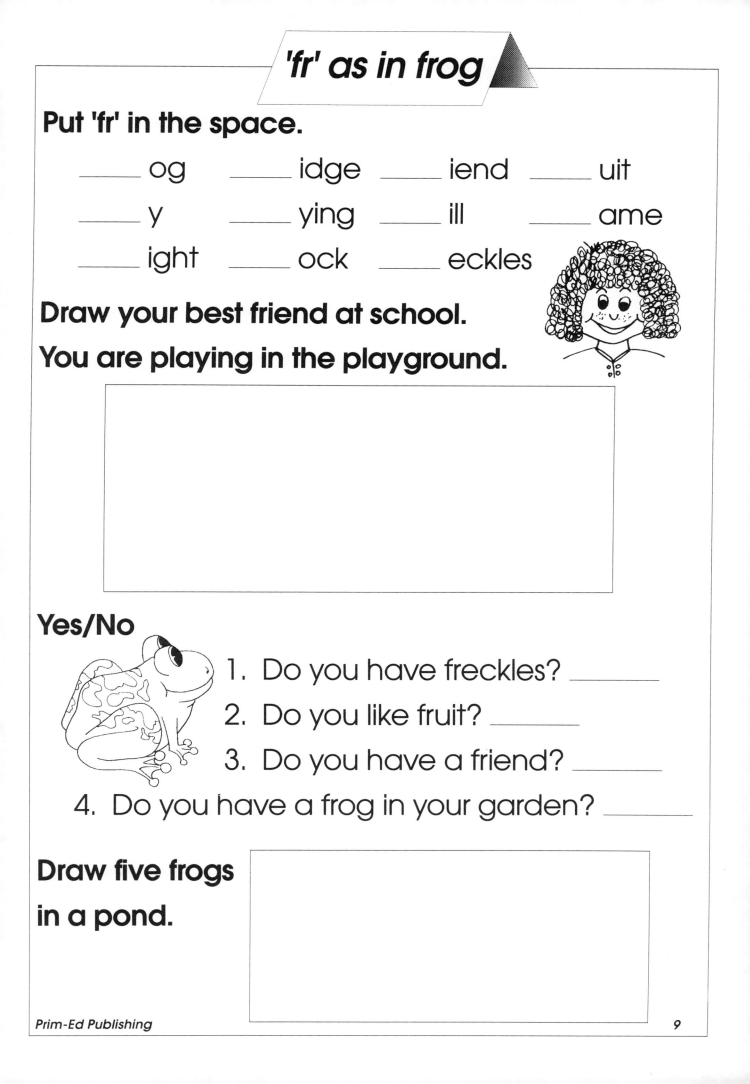

Draw your best friend at school.

You are playing in the playground.

Yes/No

1. Do you have freckles? _____

2. Do you like fruit? _____

3. Do you have a friend? _____

4. Do you have a frog in your garden? _____

Draw five frogs in a pond.

'br' as in brown

Put 'br' in the space.

_____ own _____ ick _____ idge _____ ush

_____ ushes _____ ead _____ oom _____ other

_____ eak _____ ing _____ im _____ ide

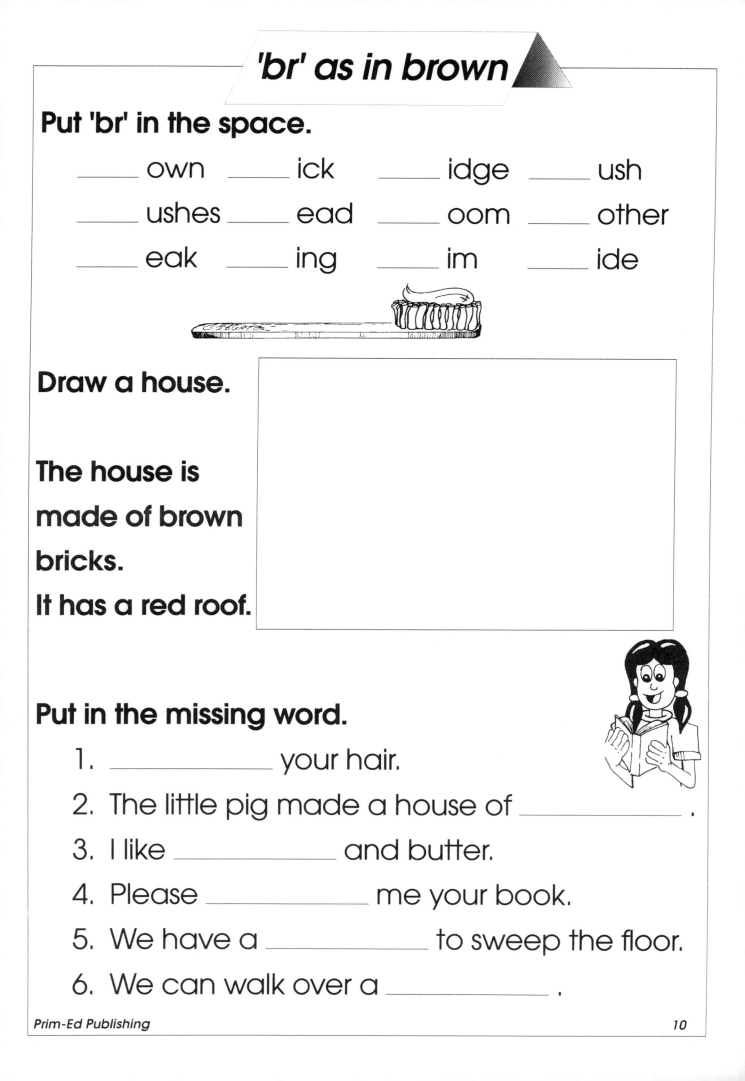

Draw a house.

The house is made of brown bricks. It has a red roof.

Put in the missing word.

1. _____ your hair.

2. The little pig made a house of _____ .

3. I like _____ and butter.

4. Please _____ me your book.

5. We have a _____ to sweep the floor.

6. We can walk over a _____ .

Put 'cr' in the space.

_____ ab   _____ oss   _____ awl   _____ ash

_____ own   _____ eam   _____ acker _____ ane

_____ ayon   _____ icket   _____ ust   _____ eep

_____ adle   _____ umpet

Put in the missing word.

1. We play _____ with a bat.

2. A _____ bit me on my toe.

3. I like jam and _____ .

4. The baby sleeps in a _____ .

5. Two cars had a _____ .

Draw a crab.
The crab has a crown.

Draw six crumpets
   on a plate.

Yes /No

Do you like crumpets? _____

Do you like crusts? _____

'dr' as in drum

Put 'dr' in the space.

_____ um   _____ ink   _____ op   _____ ess

_____ aw   _____ agon   _____ ive   _____ ibble

Yes/No

1. Have you seen a dragon? _____

2. Do you have a drum? _____

3. Can you drive a car? _____

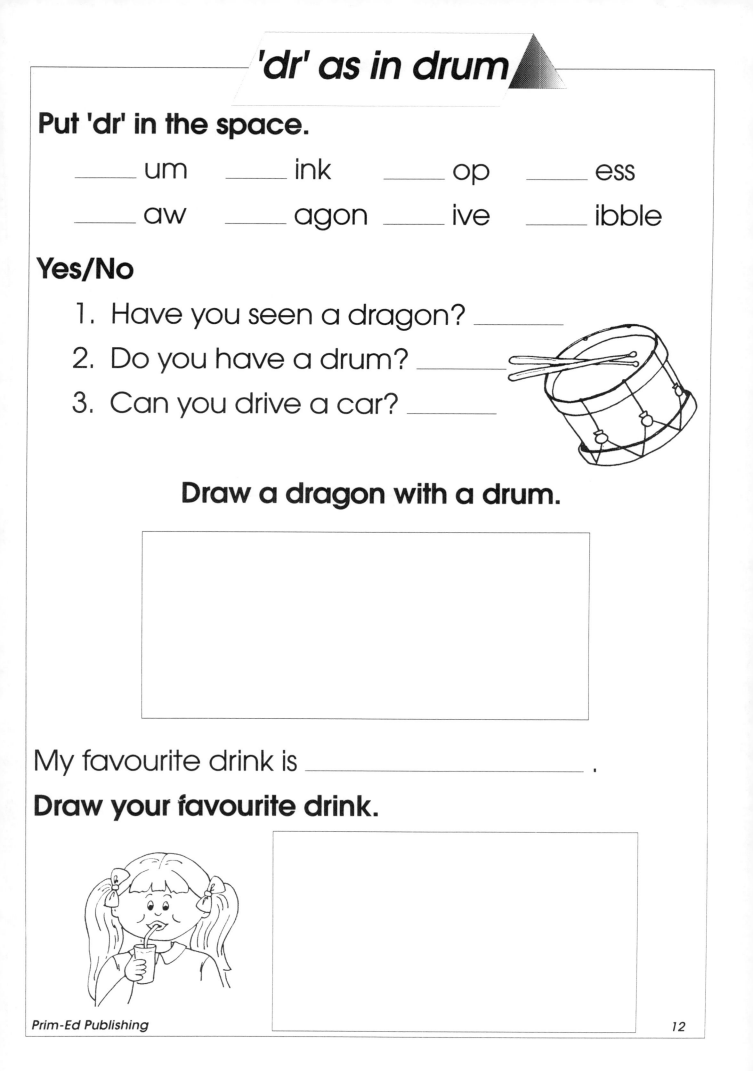

Draw a dragon with a drum.

My favourite drink is _____ .

Draw your favourite drink.

'gr' as in grub

Put 'gr' in the space.

_____ ub   _____ ass   _____ and

_____ een   _____ apes   _____ ill

_____ eetings   _____ ab   _____ andmother

_____ andfather

Yes/No

1. Do you have a grandmother? _____

2. Do you have a grandfather? _____

3. Do you like grapes? _____

4. Is grass green? _____

Draw Grandmother and Grandfather sitting in the garden.

They are eating grapes.

'gl' as in glad

Put 'gl' in the space.

_____ ad   _____ um   _____ ass

_____ ue   _____ itter   _____ asses

_____ ider   _____ obe   _____ oves

Yes/No

1. Have you seen a glider? _____
2. Do you have some glue? _____
3. Do you feel glum? _____
4. Do you have some gloves? _____
5. Have you seen a globe?_____
6. Do you wear glasses? _____

Draw Grandma.

She has her glasses on.

She has blue gloves and a red dress.

'sl' as in slide

Put 'sl' in the space.

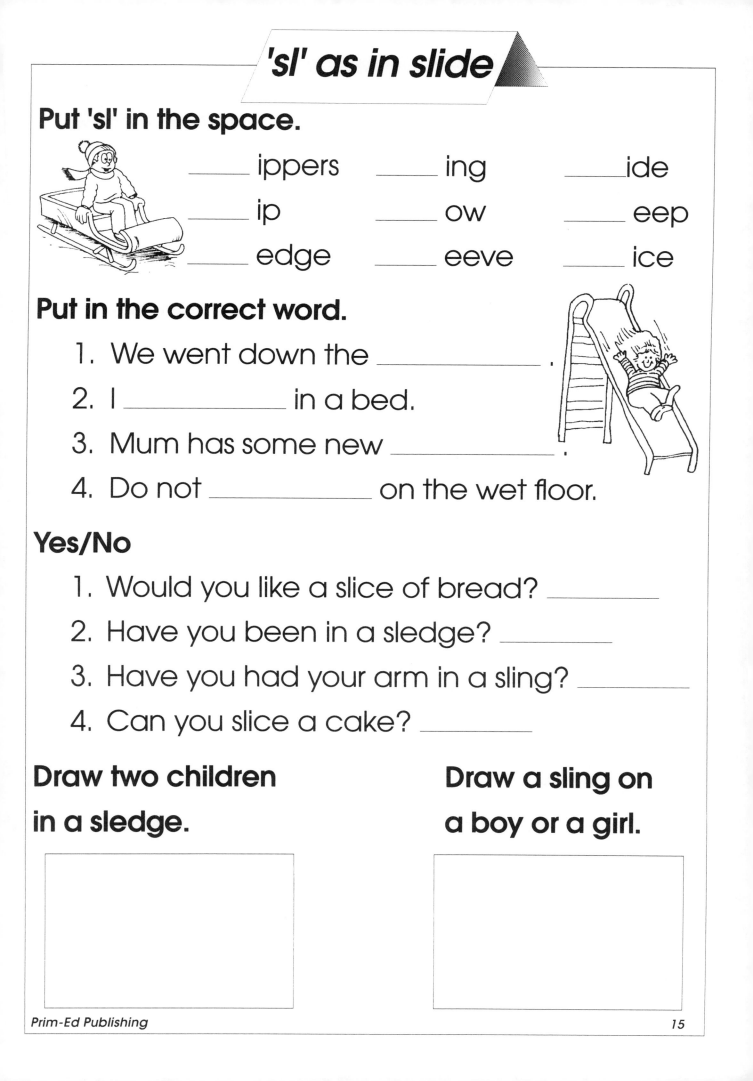

_____ ippers   _____ ing   _____ ide

_____ ip   _____ ow   _____ eep

_____ edge   _____ eeve   _____ ice

Put in the correct word.

1. We went down the _____ .

2. I _____ in a bed.

3. Mum has some new _____ .

4. Do not _____ on the wet floor.

Yes/No

1. Would you like a slice of bread? _____

2. Have you been in a sledge? _____

3. Have you had your arm in a sling? _____

4. Can you slice a cake? _____

Draw two children in a sledge.

Draw a sling on a boy or a girl.

'pl' as in play

Put 'pl' in the space.

_____ay   _____um   _____ant

_____ug   _____ate   _____ayground

_____us   _____ane   _____anet

_____op

Draw some children playing in the playground.

Draw a plant.

It is near a pond.

Draw a plum on a plate.

The plum is purple.

'bl' as in black

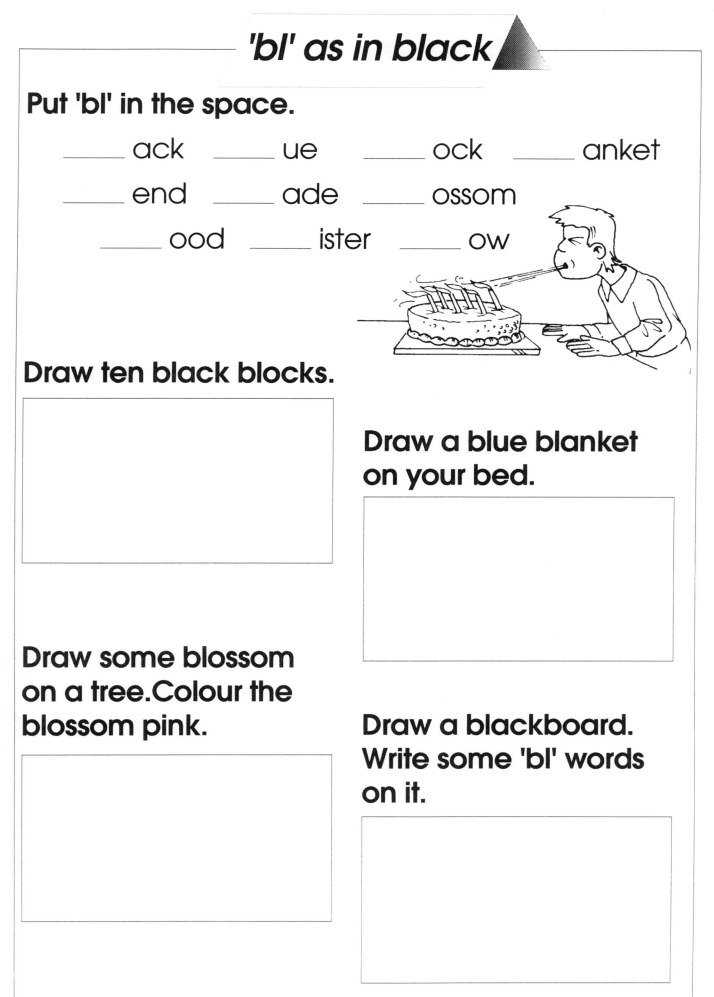

Put 'bl' in the space.

_____ ack _____ ue _____ ock _____ anket

_____ end _____ ade _____ ossom

_____ ood _____ ister _____ ow

Draw ten black blocks.

Draw a blue blanket on your bed.

Draw some blossom on a tree. Colour the blossom pink.

Draw a blackboard. Write some 'bl' words on it.

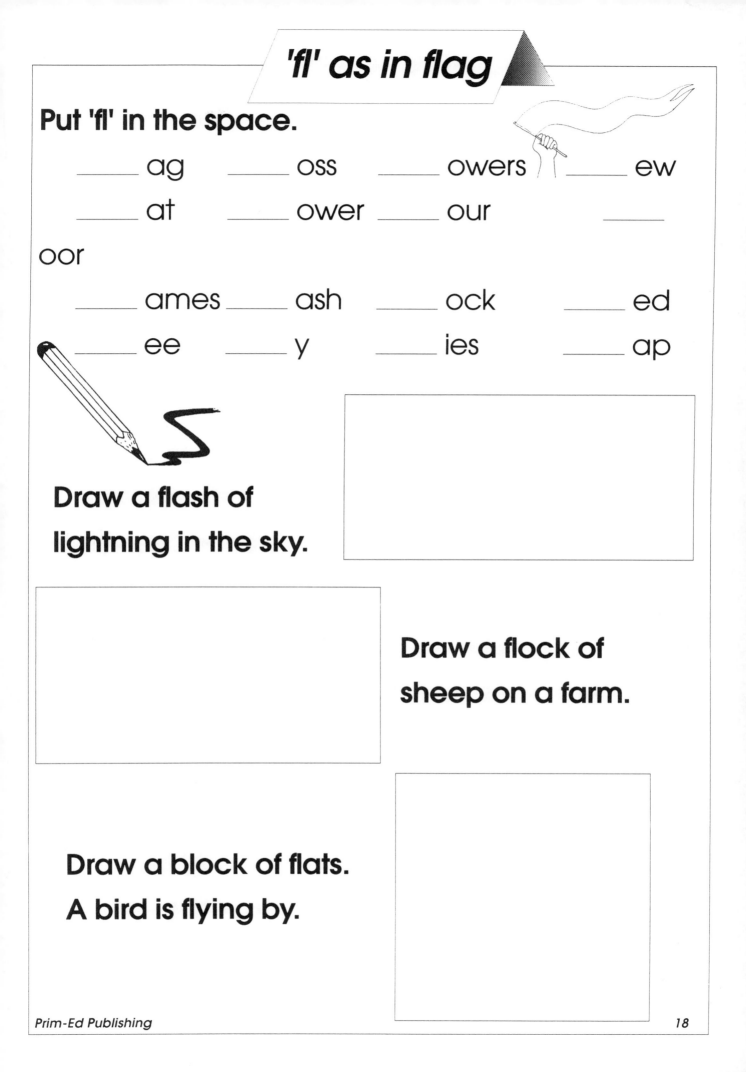

Put 'fl' in the space.

_____ ag   _____ oss   _____ owers   _____ ew

_____ at   _____ ower   _____ our   _____

oor

_____ ames   _____ ash   _____ ock   _____ ed

_____ ee   _____ y   _____ ies   _____ ap

Draw a flash of lightning in the sky.

Draw a flock of sheep on a farm.

Draw a block of flats.
A bird is flying by.

'cl' as in clown

Put 'cl' in the space.

_____ own   _____ iff   _____ ap   _____ oud

_____ am   _____ imb   _____ ock   _____ aw

_____ ogs   _____ assroom

Yes/No

1. A clown can clap. _____
2. Can you climb up the stairs? _____
3. A clock can clap. _____
4. Clogs are shoes. _____
5. A clock goes click-clack. _____

Draw some people standing on top of a cliff.

Draw a clown clapping his hands.

Put 'ing' in the space.

r _____   s _____   k _____   noth _____

fl _____   th _____   cl _____   morn _____

sw _____   br _____   spr _____   str _____

st _____   w _____

Put in the missing word.

1. Mother wears a _____ on her finger.

2. The _____ has a crown.

3. The bird hurt its _____ .

4. I like to play on the _____ .

5. Please _____ me my book.

6. Every _____ I wash my face.

7. At music, we _____ .

8. My kitten plays with a ball of _____ .

Draw a black and white kitten playing with a ball of string.

'st' as in stop and nest

Put 'st' in the space.

_____ op   _____ em   _____ ick   _____ ars

_____ and   _____ amp   _____ ill   _____ ay

_____ iff   ne _____   be _____   re _____

te _____   we _____   co _____   lo _____

mu _____   ju _____   cru _____   mi _____

Put the missing word in the space.

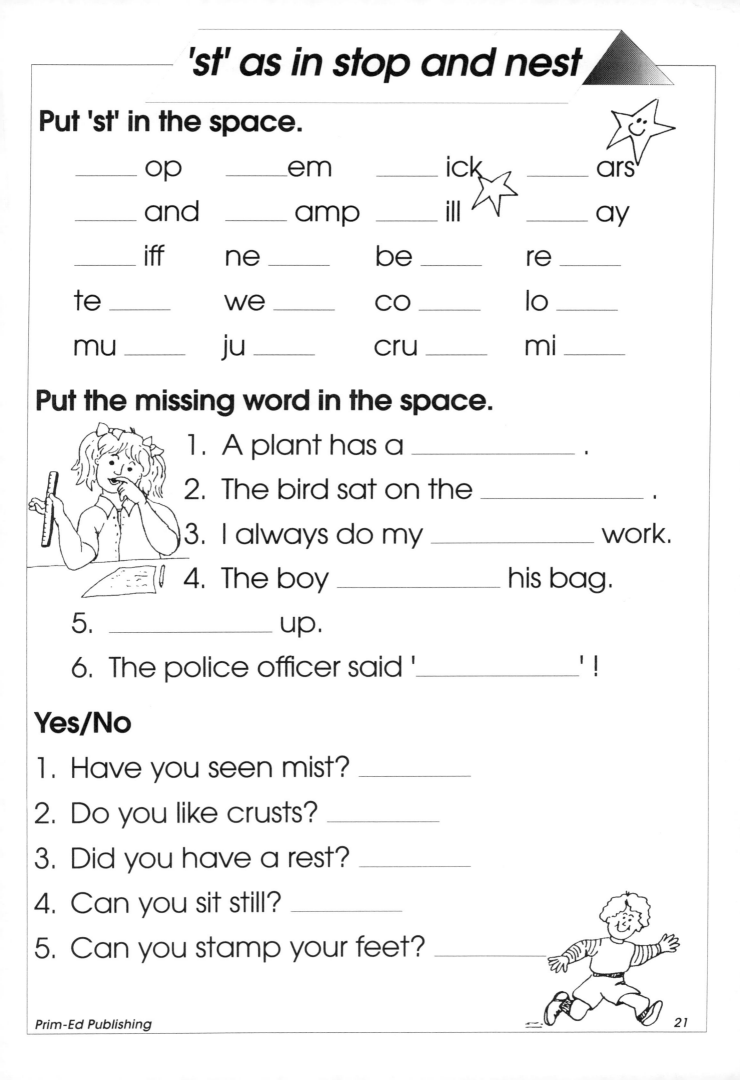

1. A plant has a _____ .

2. The bird sat on the _____ .

3. I always do my _____ work.

4. The boy _____ his bag.

5. _____ up.

6. The police officer said '_____' !

Yes/No

1. Have you seen mist? _____

2. Do you like crusts? _____

3. Did you have a rest? _____

4. Can you sit still? _____

5. Can you stamp your feet? _____

'sn' as in snail

Put 'sn' in the space.

_____ ail   _____ ap   _____ ip   _____ ow

_____ ake   _____ ack   _____ eeze   _____ owman

_____ iff   _____ ore   _____ out   _____ uggle

Put in the missing word.

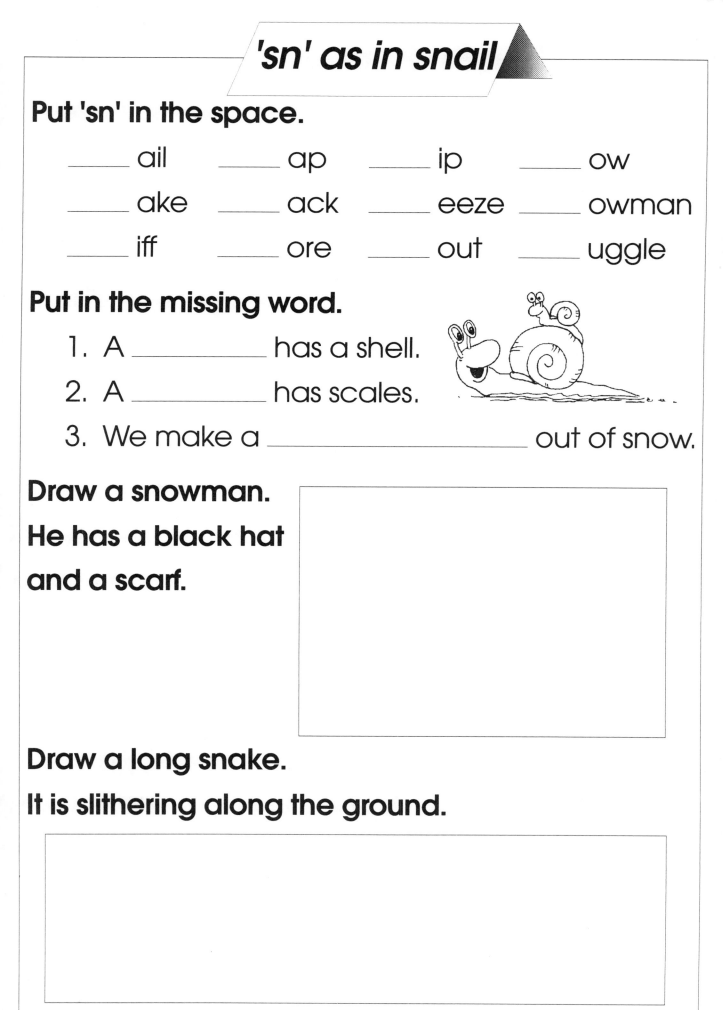

1. A _____ has a shell.

2. A _____ has scales.

3. We make a _____ out of snow.

Draw a snowman.
He has a black hat
and a scarf.

Draw a long snake.
It is slithering along the ground.

Put 'sp' in the space.

____ ot	____ an	____ ider	____ ell
	____ ace	____ end	____ ort
	____ iny	____ eckle	____ oon
____ ade	____ in	____ eed	____ ill

Put in the missing word.

1. A _____ has a web.

2. Do not _____ your drink.

3. We can _____ words.

4. We dig in the garden with a _____ .

5. We eat soup with a _____ .

6. Do not _____ in your car.

Draw a spider in a web. It has caught an insect.

Draw your class playing sport.

'sm' as in smell

Put 'sm' in the space.

_____ ell   _____ all   _____ ash   _____ile

_____ oke   _____ ock   _____ udge   _____ art

Ye/No

1. Are you small? _____
2. Can you smile? _____
3. Can you smell? _____
4. Do you like smog? _____

Draw smoke coming out of a chimney.

Draw a small clown by a tall tree.

'sw' as in swim

Put 'sw' in the space.

_____ im   _____ ing   _____ eep   _____ itch

_____ eet   _____ allow   _____ an   _____ eets

_____ oop   _____ imming

Yes/No

1. Do you like sweets? _____

2. Can you swim? _____

3. Do you like swimming? _____

4. Have you seen a swan? _____

5. Do you like playing on a swing? _____

6. Can a bird swoop? _____

Draw a swimming pool.

Lots of children are swimming.

'sc' as in scone

Put 'sc' in the space.

____ ones   ____ arf   ____ out   ____ oop

____ ooter   ____ ales   ____ an   ____ atter

____ ar   ____ ore   ____ rape   ____ rew

____ rub

Yes/No

1. Do you like scones? _____

2. Can a cat scratch? _____

3. Do you have a scar? _____

4. Do you wear a scarf? _____

5. Can you ride a scooter? _____

Draw yourself riding a scooter. You have a scarf around your neck.

Draw some scones on a plate.

'sk' as in skip and tusk

Put 'sk' in the space.

_____ y   _____ in   _____ ip   _____ ipping

_____ irt   _____ i   _____ ill   _____ eleton

_____ ull   _____ ate   tu _____   ru _____

hu _____   ri _____   de _____

Put in the missing word.

1. That elephant has only one _____ .

2. Baby likes to eat a _____ .

3. In school, we sit at a _____ .

4. We can _____ with a rope.

5. A _____ is made of bones.

Draw your desk at school.

Draw a skeleton.

'ch' as in chick and lunch

Put 'ch' in the space.

_____ ick   _____ op   _____ ip   _____ ur _____

_____ at   _____ est   _____ ill   _____ ildren

_____ air   _____ in   _____ eck   _____ imney

mu _____   su _____   pin _____   _____ eese

pun _____   lun _____   ri _____   mar _____

Put in the missing word.

1. Do not _____ or _____ .

2. We had _____ sandwiches for _____ .

3. Please _____ the wood for the fire .

4. The wolf fell down the _____ .

5. On Sunday we go to _____ .

6. A _____ says cheep, cheep.

Draw two children.

They have ten chicks in a box.

'sh' as in ship and wish

Put 'sh' in the space.

_____ ip   _____ op   _____ ell   _____ ut

_____ ed   _____ eep   _____ oe   _____ ark

_____ arp   _____ elf   _____ e   fi _____

wi _____   sma _____   fla _____   cra _____

fre _____   bru _____

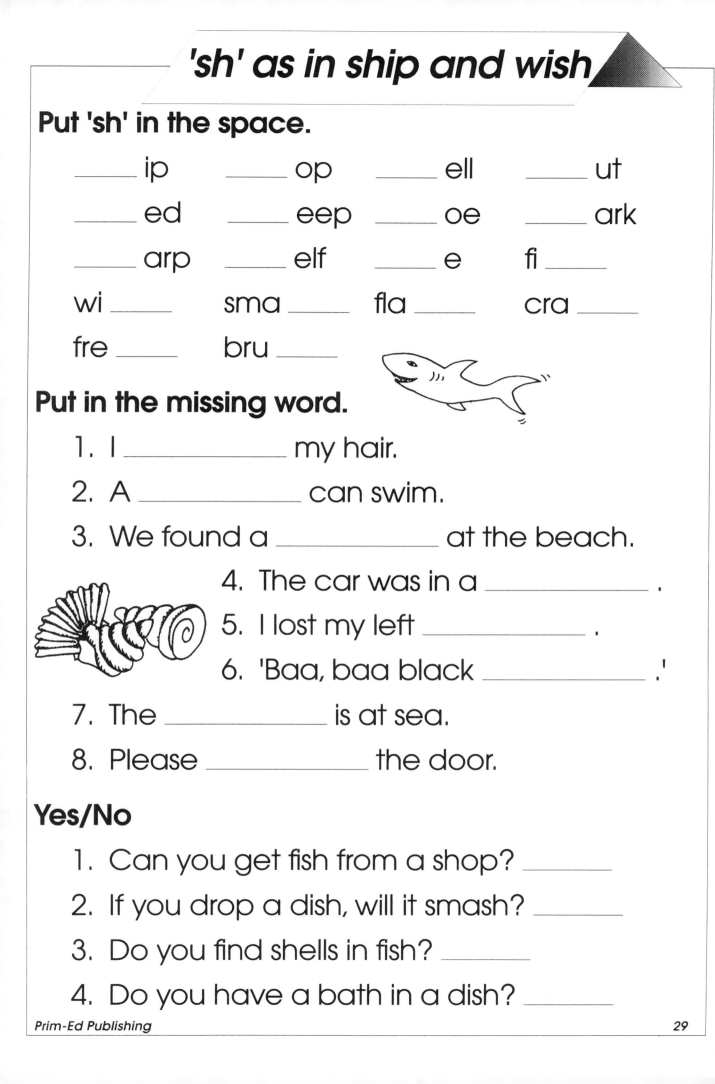

Put in the missing word.

1. I _____ my hair.

2. A _____ can swim.

3. We found a _____ at the beach.

4. The car was in a _____ .

5. I lost my left _____ .

6. 'Baa, baa black _____ .'

7. The _____ is at sea.

8. Please _____ the door.

Yes/No

1. Can you get fish from a shop? _____

2. If you drop a dish, will it smash? _____

3. Do you find shells in fish? _____

4. Do you have a bath in a dish? _____

'th' as in three and bath

Put 'th' in the space.

_____ ree   _____ is   _____ en   _____ an

_____ imble _____ em   _____ ick   _____ at

_____ umb   _____ in   _____ e   _____ under

ba _____   mo _____   tee _____   pa _____

clo _____   mou _____

Put in the missing word.

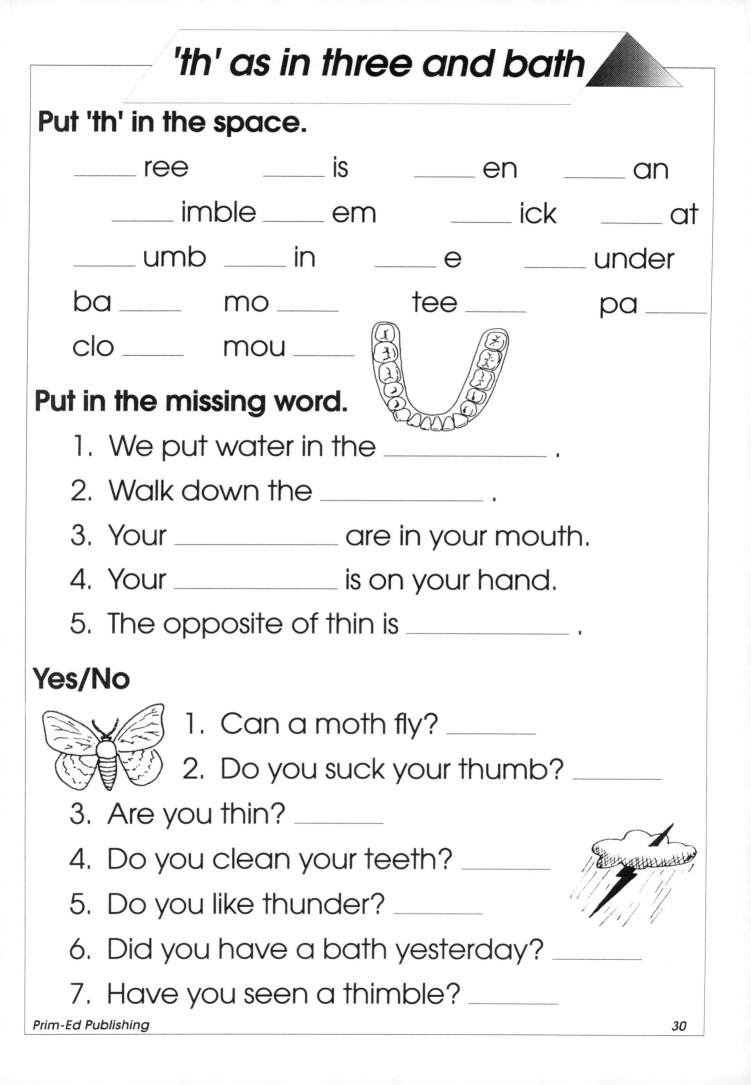

1. We put water in the _____ .

2. Walk down the _____ .

3. Your _____ are in your mouth.

4. Your _____ is on your hand.

5. The opposite of thin is _____ .

Yes/No

1. Can a moth fly? _____

2. Do you suck your thumb? _____

3. Are you thin? _____

4. Do you clean your teeth? _____

5. Do you like thunder? _____

6. Did you have a bath yesterday? _____

7. Have you seen a thimble? _____

'wh' as in whip

Put 'wh' in the space.

____ ip	____ y	____ en	____ at
____ ale	____ eel	____ ite	____ eat
____ ere	____ ile	____ iskers	____ istle

Put in the missing word.

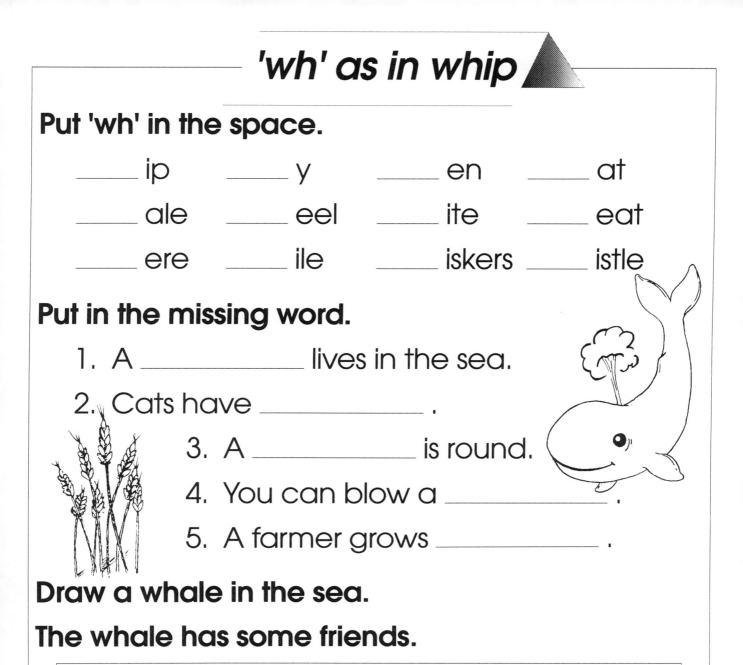

1. A _____ lives in the sea.

2. Cats have _____ .

3. A _____ is round.

4. You can blow a _____ .

5. A farmer grows _____ .

Draw a whale in the sea.

The whale has some friends.

Put 'all' in the space.

b _____   c _____   w _____   h _____

t _____   f _____   sm _____   st _____

Put in the missing word

1. The _____ bounced up and down.

2. In the toy shop there was a _____ teddy.

3. Mother will _____ us for our tea.

4. A horse can sleep in a _____ .

5. Humpty Dumpty sat on a _____ .

6. The _____ man was on stilts.

7. Do not walk on the wall because you will _____ .

Draw Humpty Dumpty sitting on the wall. A tall soldier is standing by the wall.

'ee' as in tree

Put 'ee' in the space.

tr _____   s _____   f _____ t   cr _____ p

b _____   f _____ d   p _____ l   qu _____ n

st _____ p fr _____   f _____ l   gr _____ n

n _____ d   s _____ k   k _____ p   sl _____ p

d _____ p   w _____ k   b _____ n   sw _____ p

s _____ m   w _____ p   sw _____ t   st _____ p

Yes/No

1. A tree is green. _____

2. I can peel an apple. _____

3. Cheese is green. _____

4. I sleep on my feet. _____

5. A bee can sting me. _____

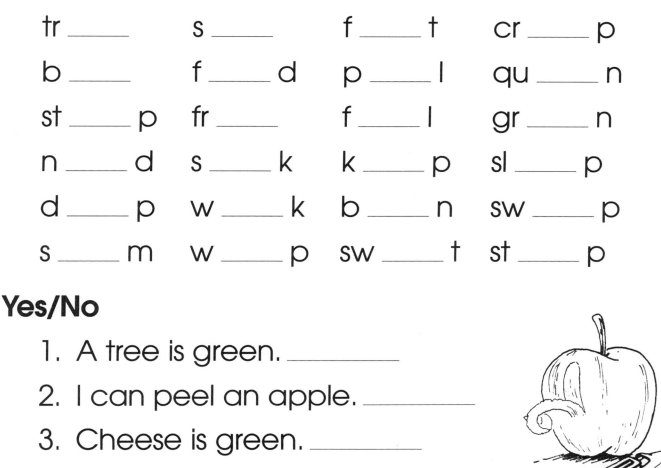

Put in the missing word.

1. We _____ in a bed.

2. Some apples are _____ .

3. I will _____ my apple.

4. Apples grow on a _____ .

5. There are seven days in a _____ .

6. I put shoes on my _____ .

'ea' as in leaf

Put 'ea' in the space.

l ___ f   cl ___ n   b ___ ch   t ___

t ___ m   r ___ ch   s ___   ___ ch

p ___ ch   ___ t   m ___ t   t ___ cher

n ___ t   st ___ m   cr ___ m   b ___ n

h ___ t   wh ___ t   fl ___   p ___

m ___ n   r ___ d   r ___ ding

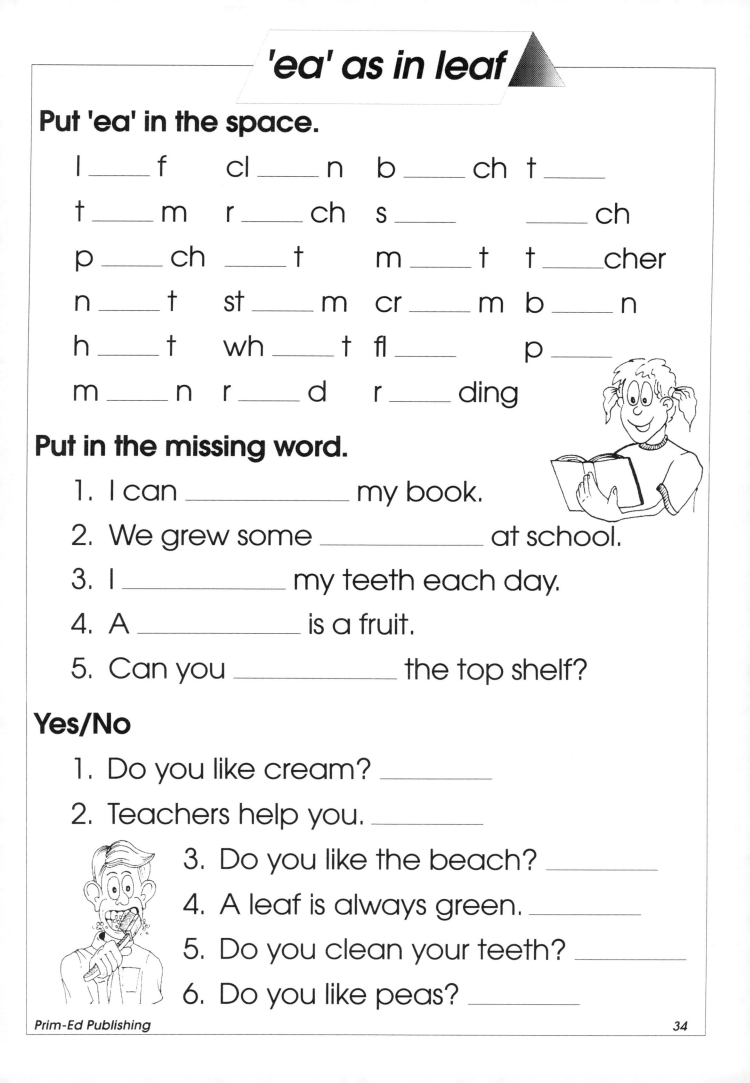

Put in the missing word.

1. I can _____ my book.

2. We grew some _____ at school.

3. I _____ my teeth each day.

4. A _____ is a fruit.

5. Can you _____ the top shelf?

Yes/No

1. Do you like cream? _____

2. Teachers help you. _____

3. Do you like the beach? _____

4. A leaf is always green. _____

5. Do you clean your teeth? _____

6. Do you like peas? _____

'ea' as in leaf (cont.)

Put 'ea' in the space.

cr ____ m   wh ____ t   s ____ side

st ____ m   fl ____   b ____ ch

1. A farmer grows _____ .
2. The _____ hopped on the dog.
3. _____ comes out of a kettle.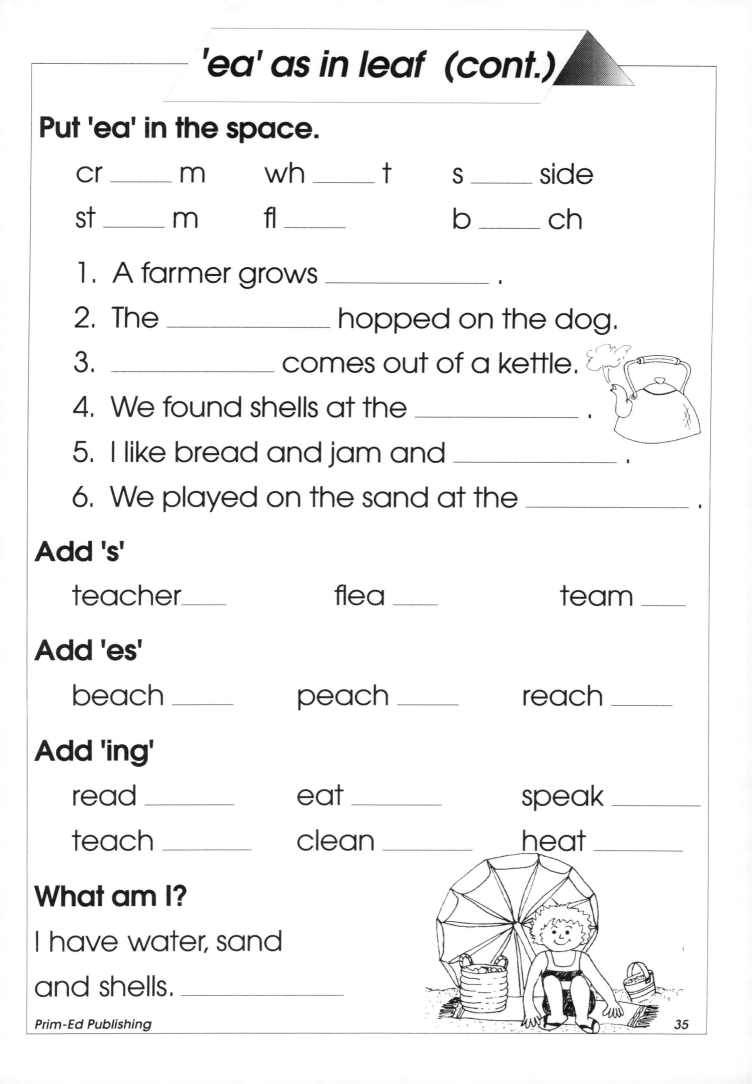
4. We found shells at the _____ .
5. I like bread and jam and _____ .
6. We played on the sand at the _____ .

Add 's'

teacher ____   flea ____   team ____

Add 'es'

beach ____   peach ____   reach ____

Add 'ing'

read ____   eat ____   speak ____

teach ____   clean ____   heat ____

What am I?

I have water, sand

and shells. _____

'ar' as in car

Put 'ar' in the space.

c _____   c ___d   y ___d   st ___t

f ___   p ___k   d ___k   sh ___k

st ___   t ___   b ___   c ___pet

f ___m   c ___t   t ___t   g ___den

M ___k   b ___k   sh ___p   h ___d

Put in the missing word.

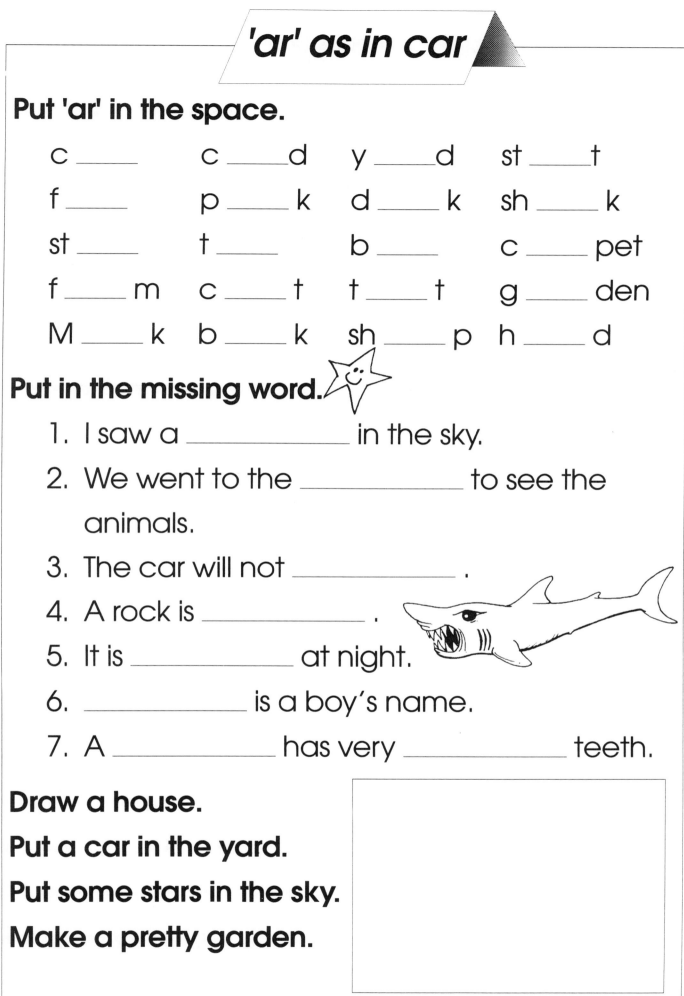

1. I saw a _____ in the sky.

2. We went to the _____ to see the animals.

3. The car will not _____ .

4. A rock is _____ .

5. It is _____ at night.

6. _____ is a boy's name.

7. A _____ has very _____ teeth.

Draw a house.

Put a car in the yard.

Put some stars in the sky.

Make a pretty garden.

'oo' as in moon

Put 'oo' in the space.

m ___ n   r ___ f   br ___ m   b ___ t

sch ___ l   ball ___ n   h ___ p   kangar ___

z ___   f ___ d   sp ___ n   t ___

p ___ l   t ___ th   st ___ l   c ___ l

t ___ t   sh ___ t

Put in the missing word.

1. You eat _____ .

2. We sweep with a _____ .

3. A _____ hops.

4. A _____ floats in the air.

5. We go to _____ each day.

6. You put a _____ on a foot.

7. Our house has a _____ .

8. I lost my _____ .

9. You can swim in our _____ .

Draw Father sweeping with a broom.

'ow' as in cow

Put 'ow' in the space.

c _____   cl _____ n   t _____ n   h _____

br _____ n   d _____ n   n _____   cr _____ n

dr _____ n   b _____   fr _____ n   fl _____ er

_____ l   gr _____ l   sh _____ er   cr _____ d

t _____ er

Put in the correct word.

1. I saw an _____ in a tree.

2. The King has a _____ .

3. The opposite of up is _____.

4. We saw a _____ at the circus.

5. A _____ gives us milk.

Can you find a rhyming word?

1. Mrs Brown went to _____ .

2. The clown is walking upside _____ .

Draw a clown riding a cow. A little brown dog is by the cow.

'ay' as in play

Put 'ay' in the space.

pl _____   d _____   s _____   st _____

p _____   r _____   h _____   aw _____

cl _____   tr _____   m _____   tod _____

br _____   pr _____   sw _____   cr _____ on

spr _____   w _____   l _____

Put in the missing word.

1. We will _____ a game at school.

2. Cows eat _____ .

3. Today is _____ .

4. We can write with a _____ .

5. On Saturday we will _____ home.

Put a rhyming word in the space.

1. Fay and May play in the _____ .

2. I came to say I cannot _____ .

Draw a sunny day picture.

Draw children playing games.

Put 'ai' in the space.

r___n   tr___n   dr___n   t___l

w___t   sn___l   n___l   p___l

p___nt   s___l   b___t   gr___n

p___n   m___n   tr___l   p___d

l___d   ch___n   h___l   m___d

st___n

Yes/No

1. Rain makes puddles. _____

2. A train goes on a railway line. _____

3. A yacht has a sail. _____

4. A snail leaves a trail. _____

5. A puppy can wag its tail. _____

6. Raincoats keep us dry. _____

Add 's'

train___   sail___   snail___   pail___

Add 'ing'

rain___   sail___   wait___

nail___   mail___   paint___

'or' as in horse

Put 'or' in the space.

doct _____   sh _____ t   st _____ k   f _____

f _____ g et   st _____ m   th _____ n   c _____ k

rep _____ t   sp _____ t   h _____ se   f _____ k

rec _____ d   t _____ ch   b _____ n   p _____ k

m _____ ning   f _____ m   t _____ n   f _____ ty

Put in the missing word.

1. I use a _____ to eat my dinner.

2. We got wet in the _____ .

3. In the _____ we get out of bed.

4. Do not _____ your book.

Yes/No

1. Do you like sport? _____

2. Do you like roast pork? _____

3. Do you like storms? _____

4. Do you like horses? _____

Draw a stormy day.

'oa' as in boat

Put 'oa' in the space.

b___t   c___t   g___t   fl___t

m___t   s___p   l___f   thr___t

t___st   r___st   b___st   ___ts

c___st   cl___k   cr___k   l___d

f___m   m___n   t___d   s___k

c___ch   fl___ting

Yes/No

1. A boat will float in the water. _____

2. You can eat oats. _____

3. Frogs and toads croak. _____

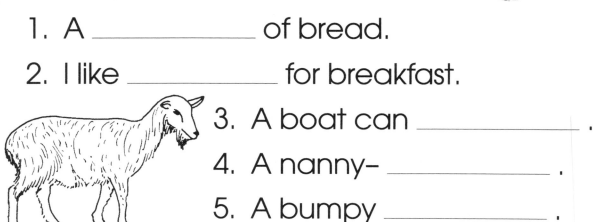

4. You travel in a coach. _____

5. Do not play on the road. _____

Put in the correct word.

1. A _____ of bread.

2. I like _____ for breakfast.

3. A boat can _____ .

4. A nanny- _____ .

5. A bumpy _____ .

6. On a cold day I wear a _____ .

'ir' as in bird

Put 'ir' in the space.

g ____ l   b ____ d   f ____ st   th ____ d

st ____   sk ____ t   sh ____ t   d ____ t

f ____   ch ____ p   th ____ ty   wh ____ l

th ____ sty   d ____ ty   s ____   b ____ thday

Yes/No

1. Can a bird fly? _____

2. Are you a girl? _____

3. Do you like birthdays? _____

4. Can you eat dirt? _____

5. Do you have a skirt? _____

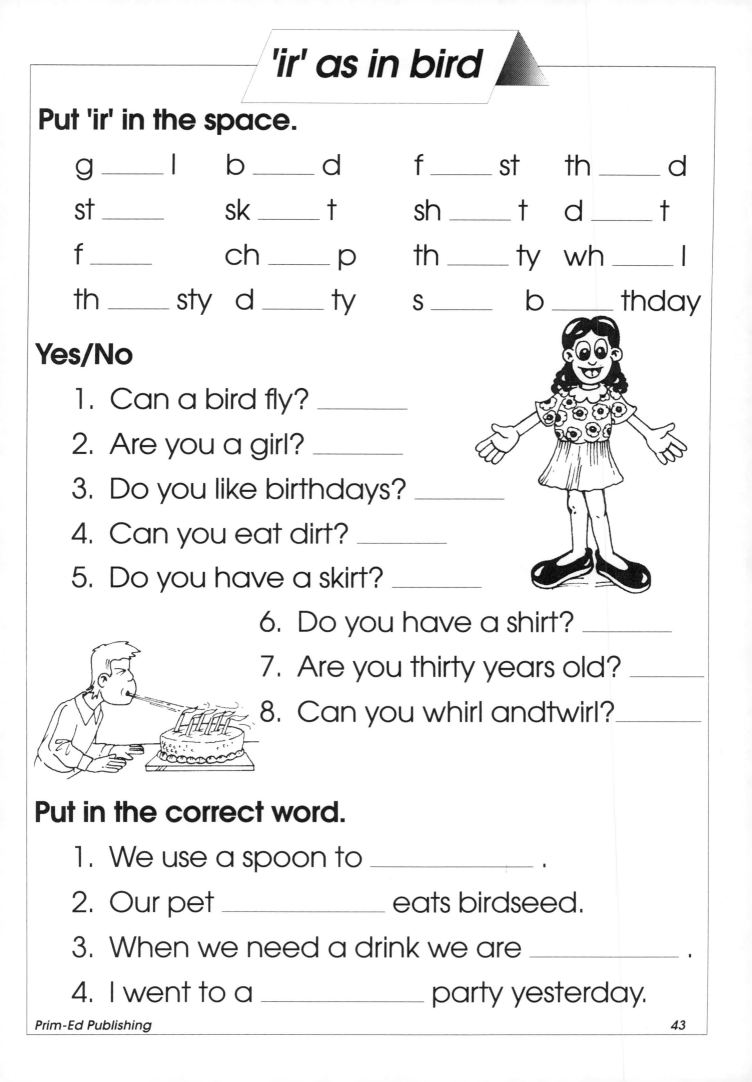

6. Do you have a shirt? _____

7. Are you thirty years old? _____

8. Can you whirl andtwirl? _____

Put in the correct word.

1. We use a spoon to _____ .

2. Our pet _____ eats birdseed.

3. When we need a drink we are _____ .

4. I went to a _____ party yesterday.

'ow' as in bow

Put 'ow' in the space.

b _____   fl _____   gr _____   arr _____

l _____   cr _____   gl _____   bl _____

thr _____   sn _____   sh _____   yell _____

              wind _____   bel _____   shad _____

              r _____   marshmall _____

Yes/No

1. Have you seen snow? _____

2. Do you like marshmallows? _____

3. Are you wearing yellow? _____

4. Can you row a boat? _____

5. Plants grow. _____

6. Have you seen a shadow on the ground? _____

Read and draw.

A snowman has a black hat.

He has a yellow scarf on his neck.

He has a happy face.

'ou' as in house

Put 'ou' in the space.

h___se   m___se   cl___d   l___d

r___nd   s___nd   f___nd   m___th

gr___nd   s___th   al___d   th___sand

___t   sh___t   am___nt   m___ntain

___ting   ___tside ab___t   sh___ting

Put the correct word in the space.

1. We must not _____ and run _____ in our classroom.

2. We play _____ .

3. The bear went over the _____ .

4. Round and _____ the garden.

5. One _____ hairy sausages.

6. Can you see a _____ in the sky?

7. We planted a tree in the _____ .

Draw a little mouse in its house.

'a-e' as in cake

Put 'a-e' in the space.

c__k__   m__k__   sn__k__   r__k__

sh__k__   t__k__   b__k__   l__k__

wh__l__   t__l__   l__t__   g__t__

h__t__   d__t__   cr__t__   pl__t__

Put in the missing word.

1. We will _____ up the leaves.

2. Please shut the _____ .

3. Mum will _____ a _____ .

4. Put the cake on the _____ .

5. Do not be _____ for school.

6. Don't forget to _____ your reading book.

What am I? Draw me.

I am very big .

I swim in the sea.

I am a _____ .

Draw a snake by a rake.

'a-e' as in cake (cont.)

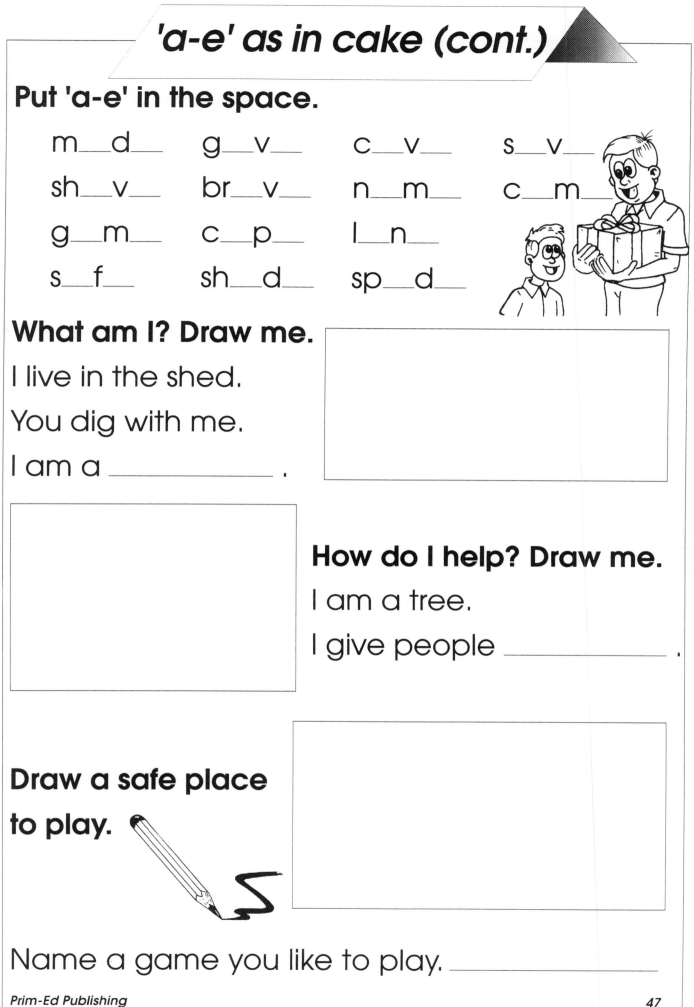

Put 'a-e' in the space.

m__d__   g__v__   c__v__   s__v__

sh__v__   br__v__   n__m__   c__m__

g__m__   c__p__   l__n__

s__f__   sh__d__   sp__d__

What am I? Draw me.

I live in the shed.

You dig with me.

I am a _____ .

How do I help? Draw me.

I am a tree.

I give people _____ .

Draw a safe place to play.

Name a game you like to play. _____

'i-e' as in kite

Put 'i-e' in the space.

k_t_	b_t_	s_t_	outs_d_
b_k_	h_k_	f_v_	h_v_
r_p_	w_p_	f_n_	sh_n_
d_c_	p_l_	l_k_	wh_t_
m_n_	s_d_	h_d_	dr_ v _
n_n_	_c_	l_n_	r_d _
l_f_	t_m_	sl_d_	sm_l_

Yes/No

1. Can you ride a bike? _____

2. Can a baby smile? _____

3. Can you tell the time? _____

4. Do you like ice cubes? _____

5. Can Dad drive a tractor? _____

6. Do you have a fishing line? _____

Draw five children playing in the park. They are all flying kites.

'o-e' as in bone

Put 'o-e' in the space.

b__n__   c__n__   st__n__   n__t__

h__m__   sp__k__   j__k__   r__p__

h__p__   w__k__   r__d__   br__k__

r__s__   h__s__   n__s__   teleph__n__

Put in the correct word.

1. We smell with our _____ .

2. It is fun to skip with a _____ .

3. I _____ my bike home.

4. The dog hid his _____ .

5. Do not throw a _____ .

6. The stone _____ the window.

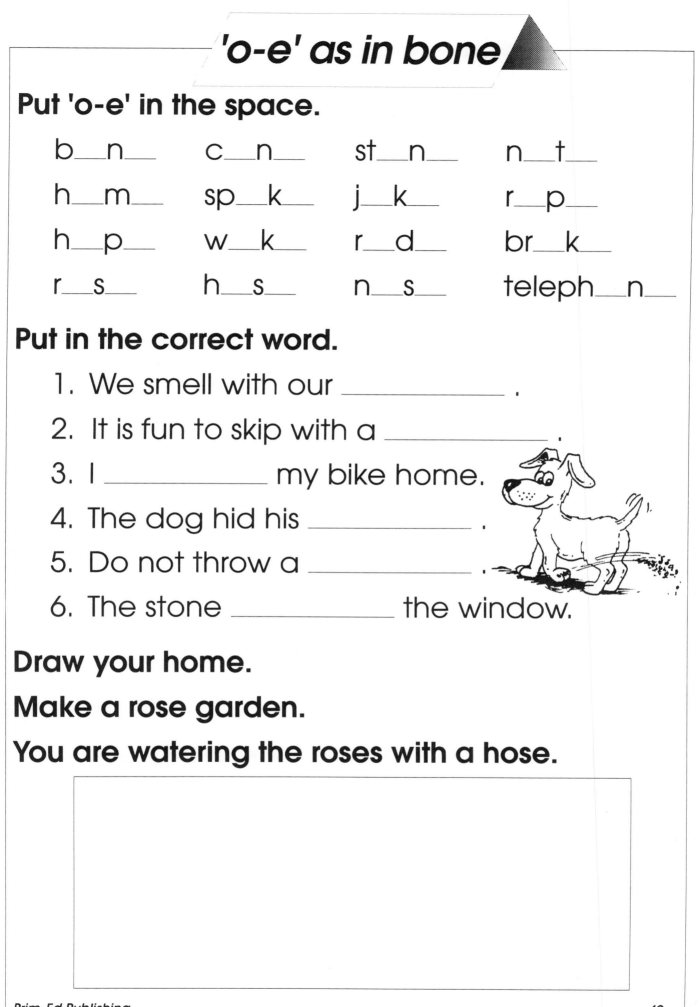

Draw your home.

Make a rose garden.

You are watering the roses with a hose.

'scr' as in screw

Put 'scr' in the space.

_____ew   _____een   _____ibble

_____amble   _____ub   _____oll

_____eam   _____ape   _____ap

_____ubbing   _____atch   _____ewdriver

_____apbook

Put in the correct word.

1. Baby can _____ .

2. Our television has a _____ .

3. Do not _____ in your pad.

4. We have to _____ the floor.

5. A cat can _____ .

Yes/No

1. Do you like scrambled eggs? _____

2. Do you scribble? _____

3. Do you have a scrapbook? _____

4. Do you scrub your nails? _____

5. Does your television have a screen? _____

6. Does a tiger scratch? _____

'spl' as in splash

Put 'spl' in the space.

_____ash _____int _____it _____inter

_____ice _____its _____atter

_____endid _____ashed

Put in the missing word.

1. Baby went _____ in the bath.

2. Dancers can do the _____ .

3. We had a _____ meal.

4. The shoes _____ .

5. Baby _____ed us with water.

Yes/No

1. Have you had a splinter? _____

2. Do you splash when you swim? _____

3. Can you do the splits? _____

Draw a swimming pool. Draw children splashing in the pool.

'str' as in string

Put 'str' in the space.

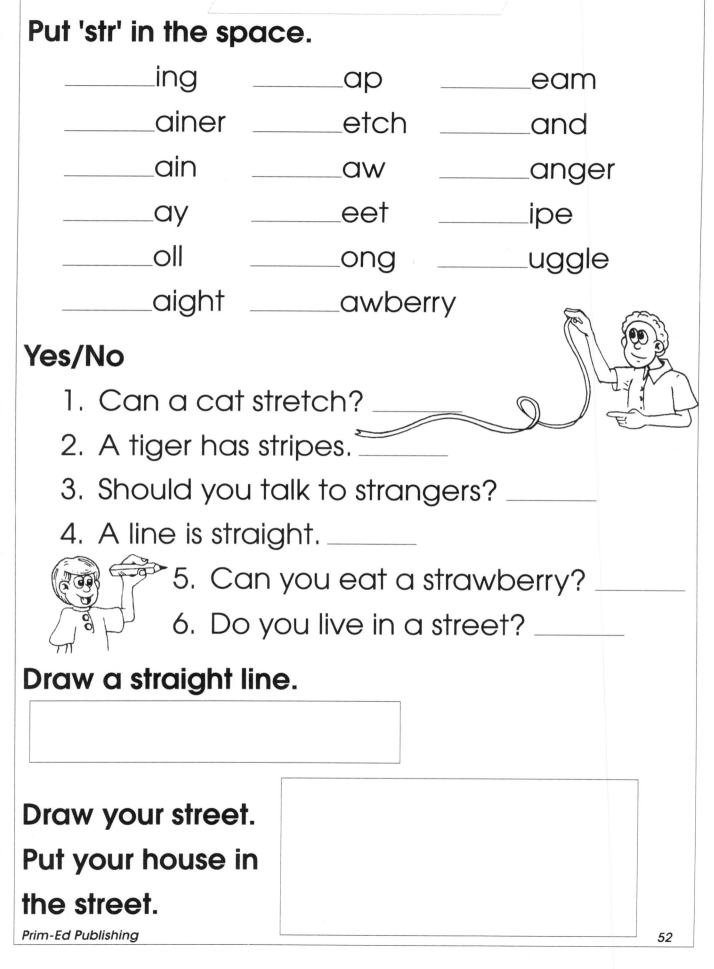

_____ing   _____ap   _____eam

_____ainer   _____etch   _____and

_____ain   _____aw   _____anger

_____ay   _____eet   _____ipe

_____oll   _____ong   _____uggle

_____aight   _____awberry

Yes/No

1. Can a cat stretch? _____

2. A tiger has stripes. _____

3. Should you talk to strangers? _____

4. A line is straight. _____

5. Can you eat a strawberry? _____

6. Do you live in a street? _____

Draw a straight line.

Draw your street.
Put your house in
the street.

'thr' as in three

Put 'thr' in the space.

_____ee   _____ow   _____oat

_____ead   _____ew   _____one

_____ough   _____own   _____ob

Put in the missing word.

1. I have a sore _____ .

2. I can _____ a needle.

3. The Queen has a _____ .

4. The lion went _____ the hoop.

5. The teacher _____ the ball.

6. We can _____ a beanbag.

7. The juggler can juggle _____ balls.

Draw three friends going through hoops.

Put 'spr' in the space.

_____ing   _____ig   _____ead

_____inkler   _____ay   _____inkle

_____outs   _____ain   _____ee

_____int   _____out

Put in the missing word.

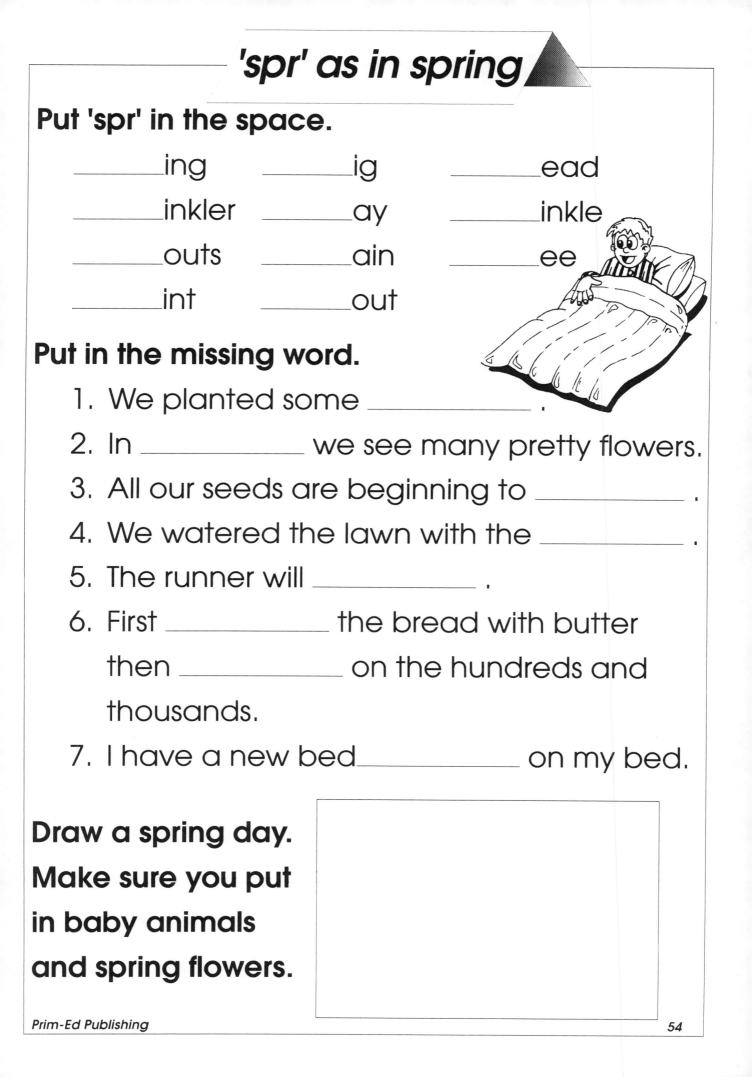

1. We planted some _____ .

2. In _____ we see many pretty flowers.

3. All our seeds are beginning to _____ .

4. We watered the lawn with the _____ .

5. The runner will _____ .

6. First _____ the bread with butter

   then _____ on the hundreds and

   thousands.

7. I have a new bed_____ on my bed.

**Draw a spring day.
Make sure you put
in baby animals
and spring flowers.**

'squ' as in squirrel

Put 'squ' in the space.

_____irrel   _____id   _____ash

_____are   _____eeze   _____ad

_____eak   _____eal   _____irm

_____iggle   _____int   _____irt

Put in the missing word.

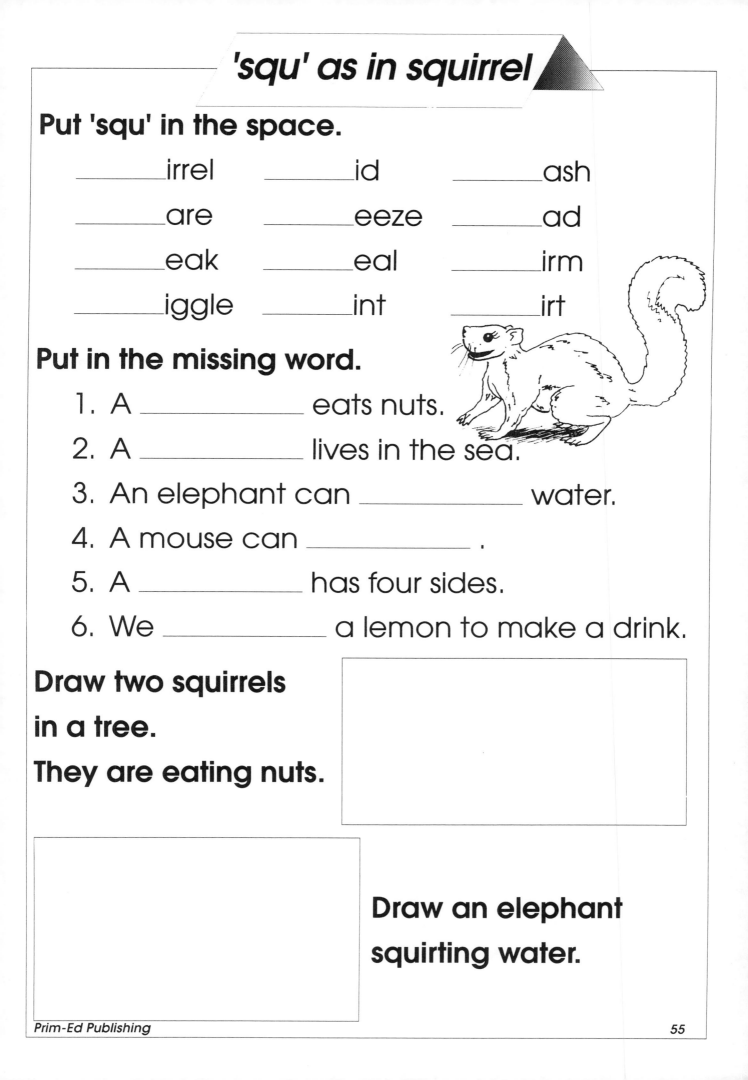

1. A _____ eats nuts.

2. A _____ lives in the sea.

3. An elephant can _____ water.

4. A mouse can _____ .

5. A _____ has four sides.

6. We _____ a lemon to make a drink.

Draw two squirrels in a tree.

They are eating nuts.

Draw an elephant squirting water.

Grades 4–8

History Comes Alive Teaching Unit

PIONEERS

A Complete, Ready-to-Go Resource Filled With Background Information, Primary Sources, Hands-on Activities, Literature and Internet Links, Mapping Activities, a Read-Aloud Play, and More!

Exciting Activities That Go Beyond the Textbook!

by Susan Moger

ISBN 0-490-13845-0

51195>

9 780439 138451

EAN